Emma Poole • Caroline Reynolds • Bob W

ESSENTIALS

Year 8
KS3 Science
Workbook

How to Use this Workbook

A Note to the Teacher

This is the second of three science workbooks for students in Key Stage 3. Together, the workbooks for Years 7, 8 and 9 provide practice of the complete programme of study for Key Stage 3 Science.

This workbook has been written to be used alongside the Key Stage 3 Science Year 8 coursebook. There are four pages of questions for each of the topics in the coursebook. The questions are grouped according to level, to support personalised learning and to enable students to track their own progress.

Included in the centre of the book is a pull-out answer booklet. It contains the answers to all of the questions in this workbook.

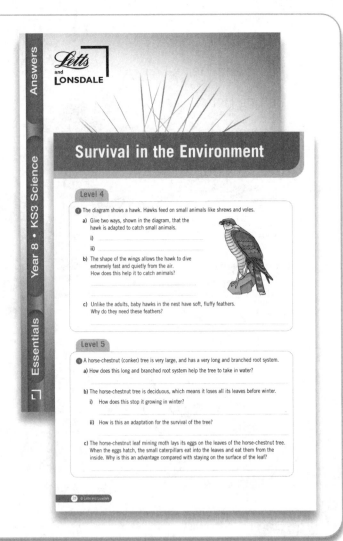

A Note to the Student

We're sure you'll enjoy using this workbook, but follow these helpful hints to make the most of it:

- Try to write answers that require reasoning or explanation in good English, using correct punctuation and good sentence construction. Read what you have written to make sure it makes sense.
- Think carefully when drawing graphs. Always make sure you have accurately labelled your axes and plotted points accurately.

- Where questions require you to make calculations, remember to show your workings. In tests, you might get marks for a correct method even if you arrive at the wrong answer.
- The tick boxes on the Contents page let you track your progress: simply put a tick in the box next to each topic when you're confident that you know it.

Contents

Food and Life

1 Some pupils put 10 identical trays of young plants in a greenhouse. Every morning they went in and gave them a little water. Four weeks later some of the plants had grown high, while others were small and weak.

a) Why did the trays need to be identical at the beginning of the investigation?

_____

b) Why did some plants grow better than others?

_____

c) Why was it necessary to grow the plants in a light place, rather than in a cupboard?

_____

2 a) Name two organs where food is digested.

i) _____ **ii)** _____

b) Why do you need to mix food with saliva?

_____

c) Why do you need protein in your diet?

_____

1 A balanced diet contains the following nutrient types:

Carbohydrates   Proteins   Vitamins   Water   Fats

a) If you eat a sweet, juicy grapefruit, give two nutrients that you would get from the above list.

i) _____ **ii)** _____

b) If you eat a sweet, juicy grapefruit, give two nutrients that you wouldn't get from the above list.

i) _____ **ii)** _____

c) Name two nutrients missing from the list.

i) _____ **ii)** _____

d) Why is it important to chew your food before swallowing it?

_____

2 Scurvy is a condition that sailors on a long voyage used to get as a result of a poor diet. A doctor thought that acid would cure it, so he carried out an investigation on four sailors. The sailors all had scurvy and were given identical diets, but the doctor gave them extra drinks. The doctor's results are in the table below.

Sailor	Extra Drink Given	Effect After Seven Days
A	Apple cider	Begun to recover
B	Vinegar	No change
C	Hydrochloric acid (very diluted!)	No change
D	Lime juice	Fully recovered

a) Was the doctor right? Give a reason for your answer.

_____

_____

b) What's the independent variable (the variable that's being changed) in this investigation?

_____

c) Why was it important to keep the sailors on identical diets?

Level 6

1 The table below gives information about four different foods.

Food	Energy per 100g (kJ)	Protein per 100g (g)	Fat per 100g (g)	Carbohydrates per 100g (g)	Iron per 100g (g)
Banana	379	1.2	0.3	23.2	0.3
Brown bread	908	9.4	2.5	41.6	2.7
Cheese	1740	25.4	34.9	0.1	0.3
Egg	612	12.5	10.8	0	1.9

a) Which of the four nutrients is needed for growth and repair? _____

b) Which of the four nutrients provides the most energy in cheese? _____

c) Which of the four nutrients provides the most energy in bananas? _____

d) Give the name of one type of nutrient not shown in the table. _____

e) Which food provides the most iron per 100g? _____

f) What does the body need iron for? _____

Level 6 (cont.)

2 a) Plants need nitrogen for growth. What type of plant cell absorbs water and nitrogen from the soil?

_____

b) Some plants, like sundew, get their nitrogen compounds from insects like ants, so they can survive on nitrogen-poor soils. Insects are attracted to the plant by a sugary liquid. Why are the leaves so sticky?

_____

c) The sticky liquid on the leaves contains enzymes. What is the purpose of these enzymes?

_____

d) Plants have green leaves for photosynthesis. Complete this equation for photosynthesis:

$$\text{_____} + \text{water} \xrightarrow{\text{sunlight}} \text{_____} + \text{oxygen}$$

Level 7

1 A student carried out an experiment to see how quickly protease enzymes would break down $1cm^3$ of jelly in acidic conditions. Protease enzymes break down proteins like gelatine in jelly. The table below shows the results for 3 test tubes she set up in a water bath.

Test Tube	Amount of Jelly	Amount of Protease Enzyme	Amount of Acid	Time for Jelly to Disappear (secs)
A	$1cm^3$ cube	$5cm^3$ fresh	3 drops	75
B	$1cm^3$ cube	$5cm^3$ boiled	3 drops	Stayed unchanged
C	$1cm^3$ cube cut into pieces	$5cm^3$ fresh	3 drops	42

a) The student kept the water bath at 37°C. Why did she do this?

_____

b) Why did the jelly in test tube C disappear more quickly than the jelly in test tube A?

_____

_____

c) Why did the jelly stay unchanged in test tube B?

_____

d) Why does protein have to be broken down in the body?

1 Salivary amylase is an enzyme that breaks down starch in the mouth. Here are some pH values for different parts of the digestive system:

Organ	pH
Mouth	6.5 to 7.5
Stomach	1.0 to 2.0
Small intestine	7.0 to 8.0

a) When food is swallowed, it goes into the stomach and the amylase stops working. Suggest a reason why.

b) i) When the food leaves the stomach and enters the small intestine, it has to be mixed with another liquid. Use the table to suggest what type of liquid this might be.

ii) What type of chemical reaction occurs when this liquid is released?

c) When digested food enters the bloodstream it causes the blood sugar levels to rise. Suggest a reason for this.

d) The blood of the vessels near the small intestine is often more acidic after a meal. Suggest a reason for this.

2 Green plants make glucose by the process of photosynthesis. This glucose is often stored as starch.

a) What group of nutrients do both starch and glucose belong to?

b) Why is the total amount of glucose made in a year by photosynthesis not all converted to plant cells in growth?

Atoms and Elements

Level 3

1. Look at the boxes below, which show how four different elements are used. Draw lines to match each element to the reason why it's used in that particular way.

Element and its Use

Iron for bridges

Aluminium for aeroplanes

Copper for water pipes

Mercury for thermometers

Reason why Element is Used

It's a liquid

It's strong and hard

It doesn't react very much and can be bent into new shapes

It's lightweight

Level 4

1. Look at the selection of substances below. One substance is an element and one substance is a compound. Draw a line to link the element to the correct substance and another line to link the compound to the correct substance.

Substances

Orange juice

Magnesium oxide

Nitrogen molecule

Salty water

Element

Compound

Level 5

1 Elements can be represented by symbols. Draw lines between the boxes to link each symbol to its name.

Symbol

| Mg |
| Cu |
| O |
| Ca |

Name

| Oxygen |
| Calcium |
| Magnesium |
| Copper |

2 Read the information below, then answer the questions that follow.

> • Sodium, magnesium and iron are elements that conduct electricity and have a shiny appearance when they're freshly cut.
>
> • Nitrogen and oxygen are gases. They don't conduct electricity.
>
> • Sulfur is a yellow solid. It doesn't conduct electricity.

a) Name an element from above that...

i) is a non-metal.

_____

ii) exists as molecules.

_____

iii) is a metal.

_____

iv) will rust if it's exposed to oxygen and water.

_____

b) Name the compound that's made when...

i) iron is heated with sulfur.

_____

ii) sodium is burned in air.

_____

3 Magnesium is a metal. Kevin heated some magnesium ribbon until it formed a white powder.

a) Which of these statements is true of magnesium? Tick the two correct options.

 A It's brittle   ◯   **B** It's a good electrical conductor   ◯

 C It's a liquid at room temperature   ◯   **D** It's a poor thermal conductor   ◯

 E It's shiny when freshly cut   ◯

b) i) Name the white powder made when magnesium reacts with oxygen.

 ii) What type of substance is this white powder? Tick the correct option.

 A Reactant ◯   **B** Element ◯

 C Mixture ◯   **D** Compound ◯

c) Magnesium is an element. What is special about elements?

Level 6

1 The diagram below shows part of the periodic table. It only shows the symbols.

a) Name the elements represented by the symbols:

 i) C is _____

 ii) N is _____

 iii) He is _____

b) Water doesn't appear anywhere on the periodic table. Explain why it doesn't appear.

c) Oxygen is an element and exists as molecules. Which one of these diagrams could represent oxygen at room temperature? _____

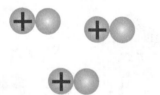 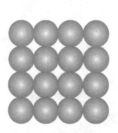 

  A   **B**   **C**   **D**

Level 7

1 These symbols represent atoms of different elements.

Look at the diagrams below. They show how the atoms are arranged in four different substances.

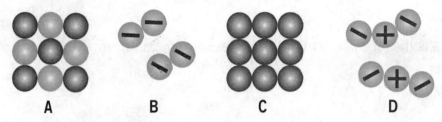

Which diagram represents...

a) a solid compound? ....

b) the molecules of an element? ....

c) a gaseous compound? ....

d) a solid element? ....

e) a substance that could be magnesium? ....

f) a substance that could be sodium chloride? ....

Level 8

1 The diagram below shows a section of the periodic table.

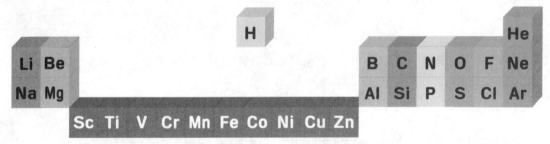

a) Name in full an element shown in this section of the periodic table that is...

i) a reactive metal. ....

ii) a metal that rusts. ....

iii) a very unreactive gas. ....

iv) a non-metal gas that exists as molecules. ....

b) Formulae can be used to represent compounds. Name the compounds represented by the formulae:

i) CuS is ....   **ii)** NaF is ....

iii) $Mg(NO_3)_2$ is ....

Getting Hotter, Getting Colder

Level 4

1 a) Temperature is the measurement of the hotness of something. What is the unit of temperature?

b) What instrument is used to measure temperature?

c) What is heat?

d) Explain why a full bath at 25°C has more heat energy than a cup of tea at a temperature of 75°C.

2 State whether each of the following is an example of **conduction**, **convection** or **radiation**.

a) A stone floor feels cold when you walk on it in bare feet.

b) Heat from the Sun travels to the Earth.

c) Only the water at the bottom of a kettle is heated but the heat travels through all the water until it boils.

d) The handle of a spoon used by a chef to stir soup gets hot.

e) A room is heated by a radiator.

f) The air in a fridge is cooled throughout, even though the cooling element is at the top of the fridge.

g) A grill in an oven heats the food below it.

1 The diagram below shows soup being heated in a saucepan on a stove.

a) Name one part of the saucepan that should be a good conductor of heat. Explain why this part of the pan should be a good conductor.

_____

_____

b) Name one part of the saucepan that should be a good insulator. Explain why this part of the pan should be a good insulator.

_____

_____

c) Suggest a suitable material for each of the parts of the saucepan you named in **a)** and **b)**.

_____

2 Hot air is lighter than cold air. This causes convection currents in the atmosphere.

a) Explain what a convection current is.

_____

_____

b) Give one example of a convection current.

_____

c) What is the name of a natural convection current in the atmosphere?

_____

1 Margaret wants to test the effect of insulating a loft, using a cardboard model of a house, some loft insulating material and a light bulb.

a) Explain one safety aspect Margaret should consider when carrying out her experiment.

....

b) Name one other piece of equipment that is needed to carry out the experiment.

....

c) Name three other ways in which someone can improve the insulation in a house.

i) ....

ii) ....

iii) ....

d) For each of the ways that you have suggested in **c)**, explain how the insulation reduces the heat loss from the house.

i) ....

ii) ....

iii) ....

e) Christos carries out a similar experiment using a different cardboard box model of a house. He has lined the walls of his box with polystyrene to represent cavity walls. He has lined the floor of his house with carpet. How might this affect the results of the experiment compared with Margaret's?

....

....

Level 7

1 A fridge transfers heat from inside it to the surrounding warmer room. This keeps the inside of the fridge cool. A fridge is called a heat pump because it pumps heat energy from a cold place to a hot place.

a) What is the normal direction of heat flow? ....

b) Where does a fridge get the energy from to pump the heat from cold to hot?

....

c) The cooling mechanism in a fridge is at the top of the fridge. Explain how convection currents in the fridge allow the cool air to reach the bottom of the fridge.

....

....

d) Selma floats an ice cube made with a coloured dye in a beaker of warm water and observes it melting. How does this demonstrate convection currents?

....

....

....

Level 8

1 **a)** Explain what the greenhouse effect is.

....

....

....

b) Explain why the greenhouse effect is important for life on Earth.

....

....

c) Explain how pollution from power stations can contribute to global warming.

....

....

d) Some people waste a lot of energy in their homes. Explain how wasting energy at home can affect global warming.

....

....

Responding to the Environment

Level 4

1 Sally accidentally stood on a sharp nail and immediately lifted her foot.

a) What was the stimulus in this action?

....

b) A sensory nerve in her foot was responsible for her noticing the stimulus. What do these nerves have at one end to 'sense' this?

....

c) She didn't have to think about this action, she 'just did it'. What is the name given to this type of action?

....

d) The next time Sally saw a sharp object on the ground, she made sure she avoided it. She had learned this and changed her .... as a result.

Level 5

1 a) The biceps and triceps are an antagonistic pair of muscles. What does this mean?

....

....

b) Look at the diagram below. Why is it important that tendons don't stretch?

....

c) If the biceps muscle contracts...

i) what does the triceps muscle do?

....

ii) which way will the forearm and hand move?

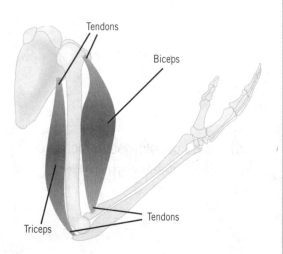

Tendons

Biceps

Triceps

Tendons

2 **a)** Complete the following sequence that occurs in a reflex action:

Stimulus ⟶ _____ ⟶ Sensory nerve ⟶

_____ nerve ⟶ _____ nerve ⟶ Action

b) What reflex action occurs when...

i) dust blows into your eyes? _____

ii) food accidentally gets into your windpipe? _____

c) 200 students were touched lightly on various areas of the arm with two pins set apart. The students were blindfolded so they couldn't see and a score was recorded if they correctly identified a touch with two pins. The number of students who correctly identified a touch with two pins is shown in the table below.

Distance Apart of Needle Points (cm)	Upper Forearm	Palm	Fingertips
1.5	112	163	178
0.5	104	119	156

i) What does this information tell you about the sensitivity of the three areas?

_____

_____

ii) What does this information tell you about the distance between the nerve endings that are sensitive to touch in the forearm?

_____

_____

iii) Suggest a reason for this.

_____

_____

3 **a)** Why does the human body need joints between bones?

_____

b) Name two different types of joint in the human body.

i) _____

ii) _____

c) Why does each joint need at least two muscles attached to the bones?

_____

1 a) This athlete is sprinting fast. Why has her heart sped up?

....

....

b) What gas is she producing in large amounts during the exercise?

....

c) At the end of the race she feels very hot. Suggest a reason for this.

....

....

d) She also gets cramp in her leg muscle. Suggest a reason for this.

....

....

e) The evening before the race she had a large meal of pasta. How might this help her run faster?

....

....

2 a) Choose from the options given to complete the sentences below.

light   receptors   sensory   stimuli   surroundings   taste

You need sense organs to detect .... to make you aware of changes in

your .... Sense organs contain .... nerve endings

with .... These can detect different things. Some nerve endings are

sensitive to touch, to .... or to temperature. Others detect sound,

.... , changes in position and chemicals in the air.

b) What is innate behaviour?

....

c) What do you call behaviour that changes as a result of experiences?

....

d) What advantage is it to a mosquito to sense heat?

....

1. The table below shows how different sports have different energy requirements.

Sport	Average Energy Needed for One Hour (kJ)
Football	2275
Tennis	1800
Running	3800

a) Explain why food reserves are used up more quickly when playing football compared with playing tennis.

b) If you don't play sport or exercise much, why are you more likely to put on weight?

c) Starch is a long chain of glucose molecules. Glucose is a single molecule. Why would eating a glucose tablet before a race be better than eating something high in starch, like bread?

Level 8

1. Hydrogen carbonate indicator changes from orange to yellow if carbon dioxide levels increase, and from orange to purple if carbon dioxide levels drop. Two test tubes were set up as shown and left in a light, warm place.

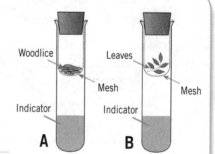

a) In tube A the indicator turned yellow.

   i) What process caused this change?

   ii) Explain what happened in this process to cause the colour change.

b) In tube B the indicator turned purple.

   i) What process caused this change?

   ii) Explain what happened in this process to cause the colour change.

c) A third tube was set up with both woodlice and leaves in it. The indicator remained orange. Explain why this was the case.

Compounds and Mixtures

Level 3

1 Draw lines between the boxes to match each mixture to the way it can be separated and the reason why it can be separated.

Mixture	How it can be Separated	Reason it can be Separated
Sulfur and iron	Pour it through a filter funnel and paper	One part of the mixture will evaporate
Salt and water	Put it in a dish and leave it on a windowsill	One part of the mixture is magnetic
Sand and water	Use a magnet	One part of the mixture is insoluble

Level 4

1 a) Draw lines between the boxes to match each type of substance with its correct example.

Type of Substance	Example
Element	Sand and water
Mixture	Iron
Compound	Sodium chloride

b) How can a mixture of mud and water be separated?

c) Which of these statements is true of mixtures? Tick the two correct options.

A They have a fixed composition ◯

B They're made of only one type of atom ◯

C They have a fixed melting point ◯

D They're easy to separate ◯

E They're made when two substances are mixed together but not chemically joined ◯

Level 5

1 Choose from the options given to complete the sentences below.

compound	condenses	freezes	mixture
nitrogen	oxygen	pressure	temperature

Air is a .... of different gases. The main gas in air is ....

Air is separated by fractional distillation. First the air is cooled down until it ....

to form a liquid. The liquid air is then warmed up. Each part of the mixture boils at a different

.... and is collected.

2 When water is heated it boils.

a) What is the change of state that takes place? .... to ....

b) At what temperature does pure water boil? ....

c) Katie wants to find out how the amount of salt added to a beaker of water affects its boiling point. Complete the table below to show the factor that Katie is going to change, measure and keep constant in her experiment.

Factor to Change	
Factor to Measure	
Factor to Keep Constant	

d) The results from Katie's experiment are shown in the table below.

Amount of Salt Added (g)	Boiling Point (°C)
0.00	100
0.25	101
0.50	102
0.75	105
1.00	104

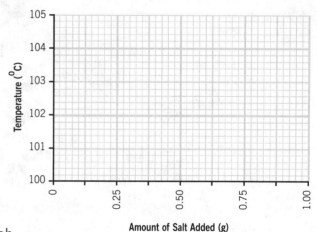

Amount of Salt Added (g)

i) Use these results to complete the graph.

ii) Add a line of best fit.

e) Write a conclusion for Katie's experiment.

....

....

1 a) Complete the table below by adding the state of each element at room temperature, 25°C.

Element	Melting Point (°C)	Boiling Point (°C)	State
A	-37	87	
B	857	1256	
C	-67	-64	
D	-5	39	

b) Why isn't butter included in this table? Explain your answer.

_____

_____

Level 7

1 These symbols represent atoms of different elements.

Look at the diagrams below. They show how the atoms are arranged in six different substances.

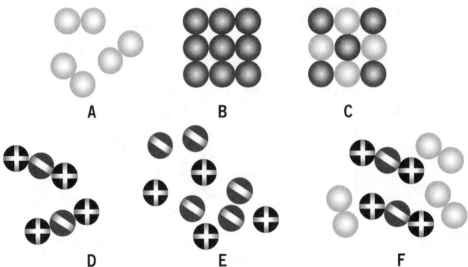

Which diagram represents...

a) a solid element? _____

b) molecules of an element? _____

c) a gaseous compound? _____

d) a solid compound? _____

e) a mixture of a compound and an element? _____

f) a mixture of two elements? _____

2 Limestone contains the chemical compound, calcium carbonate ($CaCO_3$).

a) Define a compound.

_____

_____

b) How many different elements are represented in this formula and what are they?

_____

c) How many atoms in total are represented in this formula?

_____

d) When calcium carbonate is heated, a thermal decomposition reaction takes place. One of the products made is calcium oxide (CaO). Complete the word and symbol equations below to sum up this reaction.

i) calcium carbonate $\longrightarrow$ calcium oxide + _____

ii) $CaCO_3$ $\longrightarrow$ CaO + _____

Level 8

1 Potassium nitrate (KNO_3) is used as a fertiliser.

a) Identify the elements present in potassium nitrate:

i) K is _____

ii) N is _____

iii) O is _____

b) What is the total number of atoms represented by this formula?

_____

c) Why do farmers use fertilisers?

_____

_____

d) Why is it important that fertilisers are soluble?

_____

_____

Magnetism and Electromagnetism

Level 4

1 a) Which materials below can be magnetised? Tick the three correct options.

A Iron ◯   **B** Plastic ◯

C Aluminium ◯   **D** Steel ◯

E Nickel ◯   **F** Silver ◯

G Wood ◯

b) For each pair of magnets below state whether they will **attract** or **repel**.

i) [N | S]   [N | S]   ....

ii) [N | S]   [S | N]   ....

iii) [S | N]   [N | S]   ....

Level 5

1 The field shape below shows the field lines for a simple bar magnet. Add the shape of the bar magnet to the diagram and label the north and the south poles.

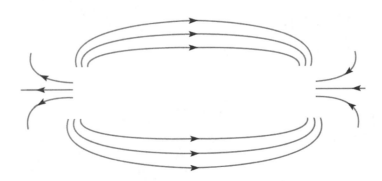

1 Look at the diagram below. Explain how each paper clip attracts the paper clip below it.

2 **a)** Give two ways in which a magnet can be destroyed.

i)

ii)

b) What happens to the domains in a magnet when its magnetism is destroyed?

c) Why does breaking a magnet in half not destroy it?

Level 7

 Mervyn has three steel bars. He doesn't know whether any of them are magnetic. He carries out some tests and finds out the following:

A is attracted to C   **A is attracted to D**

A is repelled by E   **A is attracted to F**

A   B   C   D

E   F

a) Which bars are magnetised?

b) How can you tell which bars are magnetised?

c) What can you deduce about the polarity of A and E?

2 **a)** Explain how an electromagnet is made. Sketch a diagram to illustrate your answer.

_____

_____

b) Give three ways in which an electromagnet can be made stronger.

i) _____

ii) _____

iii) _____

c) Explain what is especially useful about an electromagnet.

_____

d) Give one example of a use of an electromagnet.

_____

1 The diagram below shows an electric bell.

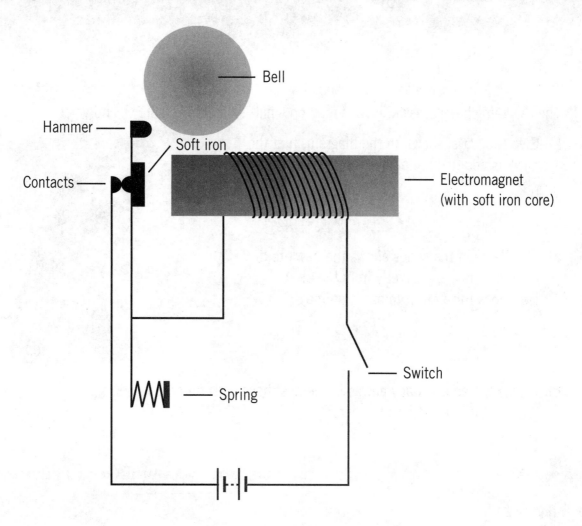

a) Explain in your own words how the electric bell works.

....

....

....

....

....

....

b) Explain what would happen if the electromagnet's soft iron core was replaced by a core of steel.

....

....

Survival in the Environment

Level 4

1 The diagram shows a hawk. Hawks feed on small animals like shrews and voles.

a) Give two ways, shown in the diagram, that the hawk is adapted to catch small animals.

i) ....

ii) ....

b) The shape of the wings allows the hawk to dive extremely fast and quietly from the air. How does this help it to catch animals?

....

....

c) Unlike the adults, baby hawks in the nest have soft, fluffy feathers. Why do they need these feathers?

....

Level 5

1 A horse-chestnut (conker) tree is very large, and has a very long and branched root system.

a) How does this long and branched root system help the tree to take in water?

....

b) The horse-chestnut tree is deciduous, which means it loses all its leaves before winter.

i) How does this stop it growing in winter?

....

ii) How is this an adaptation for the survival of the tree?

....

c) The horse-chestnut leaf mining moth lays its eggs on the leaves of the horse-chestnut tree. When the eggs hatch, the small caterpillars eat into the leaves and eat them from the inside. Why is this an advantage compared with staying on the surface of the leaf?

....

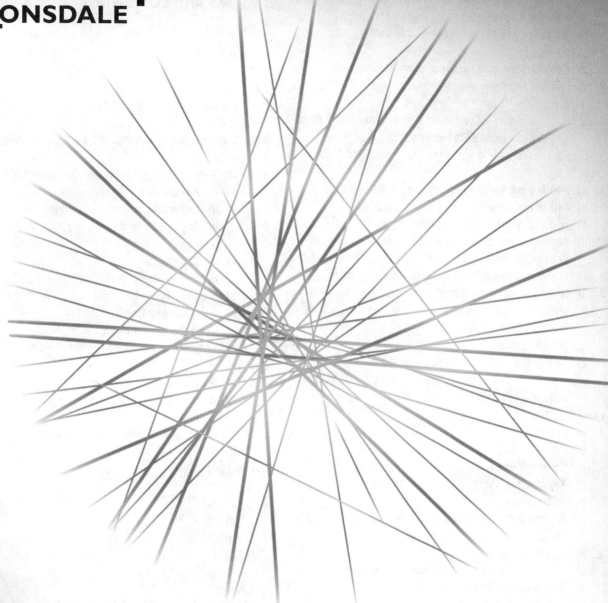

ESSENTIALS

Year 8
KS3 Science
Workbook Answers

FOOD AND LIFE

Pages 4–7

Level 4
1. a) So that it was a fair test and the trays weren't affected by anything else before the investigation.
   b) Because some plants received more water or light than others.
   c) Because they need light to photosynthesise.
2. a) i–ii) **Any two from:** mouth; stomach; small intestine; duodenum; ileum
   b) To moisten and soften the food, to help to break it down and to make it easier to swallow.
   c) For the growth and repair of cells, tissues and organs.

Level 5
1. a) i–ii) **Any two from:** water; vitamins; carbohydrates
   b) i–ii) **In any order:** fats; proteins
   c) i–ii) **In any order:** minerals; fibre / roughage
   d) **Any one from:** to soften the food; to make it easier to swallow; to break up the food; to increase the surface area of the food to enable enzymes to work on it faster.
2. a) No, the vinegar and hydrochloric acid didn't have any effect. Lime juice also contains acids but it must have contained something else too.
   b) The extra drink given.
   c) So that the doctor could tell it was the drink and not anything else the sailors ate that caused an effect (**not to make it a fair test**).

Level 6
1. a) Protein
   b) Fat
   c) Carbohydrates
   d) **Any one from:** fibre / roughage; vitamins; water
   e) Brown bread
   f) **Any one from:** for the blood / for haemoglobin in red blood cells; to prevent anaemia.
2. a) A root-hair cell
   b) To trap the insect / stop the insect escaping.
   c) To break down food materials in the insect / insect's body.
   d) carbon dioxide; glucose

Level 7
1. a) To match the temperature of the body.
   b) Cutting up the cube increased the surface area in contact with the enzyme, allowing the enzyme to work on the jelly more quickly.
   c) Because boiling the enzyme stops it working / destroys it / breaks it down / denatures it.
   d) To make the molecules small enough to be absorbed from the intestine into the blood.

Level 8
1. a) The acidity breaks down / destroys the amylase.
   b) i) An alkali
      ii) Neutralisation
   c) Starch is broken down into sugar (glucose) for absorption, so this raises the sugar levels.
   d) Protein is broken down into amino acids and fats into fatty acids for absorption into the blood, so this raises the acidity levels.

2. a) Carbohydrates
   b) Some glucose is used in respiration or converted to oils for storage.

ATOMS AND ELEMENTS

Pages 8–11

Level 3
1. Iron – It's strong and hard; Aluminium – It's lightweight; Copper – It doesn't react very much and can be bent into new shapes; Mercury – It's a liquid

Level 4
1. Element – Nitrogen molecule; Compound – Magnesium oxide

Level 5
1. Mg – Magnesium; Cu – Copper; O – Oxygen; Ca – Calcium
2. a) i) **Any one from:** nitrogen; oxygen; sulfur
      ii) **Any one from:** nitrogen; oxygen; sulfur
      iii) **Any one from:** sodium; magnesium; iron
      iv) Iron
   b) i) Iron sulfide
      ii) Sodium oxide
3. a) B and E **should be ticked**.
   b) i) Magnesium oxide
      ii) D **should be ticked**.
   c) They're made of only one type of atom.

Level 6
1. a) i) carbon
      ii) nitrogen
      iii) helium
   b) Water isn't an element – it's a compound.
   c) B

Level 7
1. a) A
   b) B
   c) D
   d) C
   e) C
   f) A

Level 8
1. a) i) **Any one from:** lithium; beryllium; sodium; magnesium
      ii) Iron
      iii) **Any one from:** helium; neon; argon
      iv) **Any one from:** nitrogen, oxygen, fluorine, chlorine
   b) i) copper sulfide
      ii) sodium fluoride
      iii) magnesium nitrate

GETTING HOTTER, GETTING COLDER

Pages 12–15

Level 4
1. a) Degrees Celsius (°C)
   b) A thermometer
   c) A form of energy
   d) Because the bath has a larger volume, it has more heat energy even though the temperature is lower than the cup of tea.

2. a) Conduction
   b) Radiation
   c) Convection
   d) Conduction
   e) Convection
   f) Convection
   g) Radiation

Level 5
1. a) The base of the pan because it should conduct heat from the stove to the soup.
   b) The handle because it should prevent heat travelling along it and burning the cook's hand.
   c) Metal for the part that should be a good conductor and wood / plastic for the part that should be a good insulator.
2. a) When the particles in a gas or liquid move, carrying the heat energy with them.
   b) **Any sensible answer, e.g.:** the circulation of hot air around a room from a radiator.
   c) A thermal

Level 6
1. a) **Any sensible answer, e.g.:** the light bulb will get very hot.
   b) **Any one from:** a thermometer; a temperature sensor
   c) i)–iii) **In any order:** double-glazed windows; cavity walls; carpets and curtains
   d) i)–iii) **In any order:** double-glazed windows – prevent heat loss by trapping the air in between the glass layers and reducing convection; cavity walls – trap air, reducing the movement of air; carpets and curtains – trap air, reducing heat loss by convection.
   e) Christos's house will lose less heat because it is better insulated, both with or without the loft insulation.

Level 7
1. a) From hot to cold
   b) It uses electrical energy.
   c) The air is cooled by the element and sinks to the bottom of the fridge because it's heavier. The hotter air takes its place next to the element and is cooled. The air cycles until the fridge is cool.
   d) The dye from the ice cube will sink to the bottom of the beaker and the warmer water will rise to the top. The dye and water will continue to circulate until the dye is distributed evenly.

Level 8
1. a) The Earth's atmosphere acts like the glass in a greenhouse, trapping energy from the Sun. The Sun is very hot and radiates high-energy radiation that can pass through the atmosphere. The Earth isn't so hot and radiates infrared radiation of lower energy that can't pass back through the atmosphere. The energy is trapped and the Earth heats up.
   b) Without the greenhouse effect, the Earth wouldn't be warm enough for life to exist.
   c) Polluting gases, such as carbon dioxide, from power stations increase the greenhouse effect.
   d) Wasting energy means that the power stations have to produce more energy than necessary. As a result, they produce more polluting gases and increase global warming.

RESPONDING TO THE ENVIRONMENT
Pages 16–19

Level 4
1. a) The nail
   b) Receptors
   c) Reflex / innate
   d) behaviour

Level 5
1. a) One muscle pulls the arm one way and the other muscle pulls it the other way; the two muscles work opposite to each other to move the arm up and down.
   b) If the tendons stretched, the forearm (or bones) wouldn't move / the force of the muscle would be less / the muscle would have little or no effect.
   c) i) Relaxes (**not expands**)
      ii) Upwards
2. a) Receptor; Relay; Motor
   b) i) You blink / close your eyes.
      ii) You cough.
   c) i) The fingertips are the most sensitive, then the palm, then the forearm.
      ii) Although some nerve endings are close together, others will be further apart (as shown by the lower sensitivity to two points 0.5cm apart).
      iii) The fingertips are always touching things, but the forearm doesn't have to be very sensitive.
3. a) To allow movement.
   b) i)–ii) **In any order:** hinge; ball and socket (**accept sliding or fixed**)
   c) It needs one muscle to pull the bone one way and one muscle to pull it back again (because muscles can't push).

Level 6
1. a) To pump the blood faster, and to get more oxygen and glucose to her muscles.
   b) Carbon dioxide
   c) Respiration and muscle contractions generate heat.
   d) Her muscles were fatigued because they didn't get enough glucose or oxygen during the race.
   e) Glucose is needed for energy, and pasta is a carbohydrate that would give her a good supply of glucose for respiration.
2. a) stimuli; surroundings; sensory; receptors; taste / light; light / taste
   b) Behaviour that's instinctive / instant / unlearned / caused by genes.
   c) Learned behaviour
   d) It enables the mosquito to detect exposed skin so that it can bite to feed.

Level 7
1. a) Football requires more energy in respiration, so it uses up food reserves more quickly.
   b) You don't use up much energy and food reserves are more likely to build up.
   c) Glucose doesn't have to be broken down, so it is easily digested and quickly available to the body. Starch has to be broken down, so it wouldn't be available to the body so quickly.

Level 8

1. **a)** **i)** Respiration
   ii) Glucose was being combined with oxygen, causing carbon dioxide to be released.
   b) **i)** Photosynthesis
   ii) The leaves were using up carbon dioxide to make glucose.
   c) Both respiration in the woodlice and photosynthesis in the leaves were occurring. The carbon dioxide released by the woodlice was being used by the leaves at the same rate, so there was no overall change in carbon dioxide levels in the tube.

COMPOUNDS AND MIXTURES

Pages 20–23

Level 3

1. Sulfur and iron – Use a magnet – One part of the mixture is magnetic; Salt and water – Put it in a dish and leave it on a windowsill – One part of the mixture will evaporate; Sand and water – Pour it through a filter funnel and paper – One part of the mixture is insoluble.

Level 4

1. **a)** Element – Iron; Mixture – Sand and water; Compound – Sodium chloride
   b) Filter it.
   c) D and E **should be ticked**.

Level 5

1. mixture; nitrogen; condenses; temperature
2. **a)** liquid; gas
   b) 100°C
   c)

Factor to Change	Amount of salt
Factor to Measure	Boiling temperature
Factor to Keep Constant	Volume of water

   d) **i)–ii)**

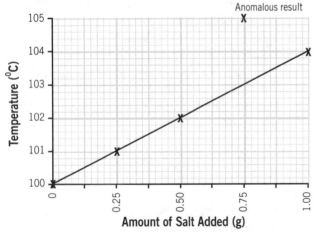

   e) The more salt that's added, the higher the temperature at which water boils.

Level 6

1. **a)**

Element	Melting Point (°C)	Boiling Point (°C)	State
A	-37	87	Liquid
B	857	1256	Solid
C	-67	-64	Gas
D	-5	39	Liquid

b) Butter is a mixture so it doesn't melt and boil at specific temperatures. It melts and boils across a range of temperatures.

Level 7

1. **a)** B
   b) A
   c) D
   d) C
   e) F
   f) E
2. **a)** A substance in which atoms of two or more different elements are joined together chemically.
   b) Three – calcium, carbon and oxygen.
   c) Five
   d) **i)** carbon dioxide
   ii) CO_2

Level 8

1. **a)** **i)** potassium
   ii) nitrogen
   iii) oxygen
   b) Five
   c) To replace nutrients that plants have used up as they grow; to help plants grow better and yield more crops.
   d) So they can dissolve in water and the plants can then take them up through the roots.

MAGNETISM AND ELECTROMAGNETISM

Pages 24–27

Level 4

1. **a)** A, D and E **should be ticked**.
   b) **i)** Attract
   ii) Repel
   iii) Repel

Level 5

1.

N	S

North pole   South pole

Level 6

1. If a magnetic material is held near a magnet, it will be magnetised. The paper clips are magnetised by the magnet and each one attracts the paper clip below it.
2. **a)** **i)–ii)** **In any order:** by banging it with a hammer; by heating it
   b) The domains change from being lined up in the same direction to being arranged randomly.
   c) It simply creates two new, smaller magnets.

Level 7

1. **a)** Bars A/B and E/F.
   b) Because A and E repel.
   c) They must be of the same magnetic polarity.
2. **a)** A coil of wire will become magnetic when a direct current is passed through the coil.

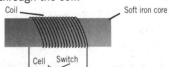

   (The answer would be correct with or without the core)

   b) **i)–iii)** **In any order:** increasing the number of turns of the coil; increasing the current; adding the soft iron core

c) It can be switched on and off.

d) **Any sensible answer, e.g.:** circuit breakers; electric bells; electric motors; loudspeakers; generators in power stations; credit cards; imaging scanners in hospitals

Level 8

1. a) **A model answer would be:** When the switch is closed, the electromagnet is switched on and attracts the soft iron. This pulls the hammer, which strikes the bell. But when the hammer moves, the contacts are pulled apart, breaking the circuit. The current stops flowing and the electromagnet loses its magnetism. The contacts are pulled back together by the spring, switching the electromagnet back on. The repeated cycle of the hammer striking the bell makes the ring of the bell.

b) The steel would become permanently magnetised and the hammer would be unable to move.

SURVIVAL IN THE ENVIRONMENT

Pages 28–31

Level 4

1. a) **i)–ii) Any two from:** curved / sharp beak; sharp claws; eyes facing forward

b) It gives the hawk the speed it needs to catch animals before they can run away; the prey can't hear the hawk diving.

c) To keep warm as the baby hawks don't move very much.

Level 5

1. a) **Any one from:** it can reach wide and deep into the soil; it has a large surface area; it has a large number of root-hair cells.

b) i) It stops making food because it can't photosynthesise.

ii) It doesn't need to use much energy during the winter.

c) The caterpillars avoid being seen by birds / predators.

2. a) Their (blond) hair and (blue) eyes.

b) Their hobbies (reading or video games), scars, best subjects and their ability in different sports.

c) **Any one from:** Yes – Their ability to play sport because they're both good, but in different sports; No – Their hair and eye colours are definitely genetic factors and all the other characteristics are very different, so they are not likely to be influenced by genes.

Level 6

1. a) **Any one from:** the eggshell protects the developing turtle; it allows oxygen in and carbon dioxide out; it allows the developing turtle to breathe; it stops infection (**not keeps it warm**).

b) i) Incubate the eggs at 35°C or above (**accept above 32°C, but not at 32°C**).

ii) **Any answer between 27°C and 28.5°C.**

iii) Because the species is endangered, it would ensure that more females would lay eggs and increase the numbers of turtles.

2. a) **Any one from:** they hide it from predators; they stop it from being eaten; they camouflage it; they keep it warm.

b) inherit; genes; nuclei / nucleus

Level 7

1. a) i) It sticks out from the flower to catch the wind; it's loose to blow around in the wind.

ii) It's relatively large and feather-like to act as a 'net' to catch the pollen.

b) It stops the flower pollinating itself.

c) The colour attracts the insects – grass doesn't have to attract insects.

Level 8

1. a) It reduces evaporation from the leaves.

b) It helps the cactus to store water.

c) It prevents water evaporating from the stem surface.

d) It helps the cactus to gain access to as much water in the soil as possible.

e) The curling keeps the leaf surface away from the wind to reduce evaporation and also raises humidity inside the curled leaf.

2. a) To transport glucose / oxygen / carbon dioxide around the body.

b) As a store of energy for use in respiration when needed.

ROCKS AND WEATHERING

Pages 32–35

Level 3

1. Slate for roof tiles – It's waterproof and can be split into layers; Limestone for making statues – It's easy to carve; Rock salt for gritting roads – It lowers the freezing point of water; Marble for making kitchen worktops – It can be polished to give a smooth, attractive surface

Level 4

1. a) D and E **should be ticked.**

b) i)

Mass at Start (g)	1.7
Mass After it has been put into Water (g)	2.1
Difference in Mass (g)	0.4

ii) It's porous so water gets into the holes / gaps between the particles.

Level 5

1. a) i) Bones / skeletons; shells

ii) D **should be ticked.**

b) i) Freeze-thaw

ii) Water gets into cracks. The temperature drops and the water freezes to form ice. The ice expands forcing the cracks open wider.

2. a) Sedimentary

b) It contains dissolved carbon dioxide.

c) Gases, such as sulfur dioxide and nitrogen oxides, dissolve in the rainwater to form acid rain / lower the pH. The acid then reacts with minerals, such as calcium carbonate, in the rocks.

d) Limestone contains calcium carbonate, which reacts with acids.

Level 6

1. a) Three

b) They're porous, so they have holes and air was coming out of them.

c) Weigh the rocks after they had been in the acid. The sandstone wouldn't react but the limestone would – one of the products would be carbon dioxide, so the mass would drop as the gas escaped.

2. a) Oxygen
   b) Global warming (**accept greenhouse effect**)
   c) sulfur + oxygen $\longrightarrow$ sulfur dioxide
   d) Acid rain

Level 7

1. a) **Any one from:** carbon; hydrogen; sulfur
   b) They take millions of years to form, which is much slower than the rate they're being used up.
   c) Because it depends on how quickly the fossil fuels are used up and how many more supplies are found.
   d) $C + O_2 \longrightarrow CO_2$

2. a) It forms when water that contains dissolved salts evaporates.
   b) The higher the temperature, the faster the water evaporates, so the faster the mineral forms.

Level 8

1. a) Grains of sediment are deposited in layers. The lower layers become compressed. Water is squeezed out and the dissolved salts stick the grains together.
   b) i) calcium sulfate; carbon dioxide; water
   ii) $CaSO_4$; CO_2; H_2O
   iii) Nine
   c) i) The quartz is very hard and hasn't weathered.
   ii) Water is squeezed out and the dissolved salts stick the grains together.
   iii) They have rubbed against each other.

LIGHT RAYS

Pages 36–39

Level 4

1. A, B and D **should be ticked.**

2. a) A **should be ticked.**
   b) B

3. a) It's transparent.
   b) It's opaque.
   c) It allows some light to pass through it.

Level 5

1. a) Light from the Sun reflects off the Moon, enabling you to see it.
   b) Stars are luminous – they give off their own light.
   c) i)–ii) Any sensible answers, e.g.: candle; torch; light bulb

2. a) Because it speeds up.
   b) Because it slows down.
   c) Refraction
   d) The stone appears shallower than it really is.
   e)

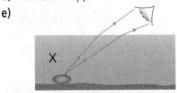

Level 6

1. a) The cat is opaque and the light can't pass through it, creating a shadow behind it.

b) Light travels in straight lines.
c) The light from the street light reflects off the cat, enabling the person to see it.
d) The speed of light is very fast, almost instantaneous.

Level 7

1. a)–b)

2. a) i)

ii) Scattering
b) The rays of light are reflected regularly, enabling an image to be seen.

Level 8

1. a) The constituent colours of white light spread out. Each colour has a different wavelength.
   b) When light passes through a prism, all the colours of different wavelengths are spread out because each wavelength is refracted by a slightly different amount.
   c) All the light is absorbed.
   d) Light of the wavelength that you see as red is reflected and all the wavelengths of other colours are absorbed.

ENVIRONMENTAL RELATIONSHIPS

Pages 40–43

Level 4

1. a) Grasshopper
   b) The insecticide would be consumed by the insect when it eats the plant.
   c) The large numbers of young mean that they don't all get eaten by foxes / predators.
   d) It provides more protection from the weather; it keeps the young warmer; the shrews are less easily found by foxes / predators.

2. a) i)–ii) Any two from: air / soil temperature; light levels; soil pH; amount of water in the soil; humidity
   b) Quadrats
   c) i)–ii) Any two from: nets; pooters; pitfall traps; sticky traps
   d) A key

Level 5

1. a) Any one from: it's a much bigger sample so a larger amount of data is collected; one garden may not be typical; one person could 'make up' the information.
   b) i)–ii) Any two from: the time of year / season; the length of the survey (one hour); only gardens are being observed.
   c) No. The RSPB would need to use more than two years of data to be sure the number was falling; it might have simply been a 'bad day' for the robins, so fewer were seen; the climate may have been different in one of the years, affecting the number of robins.

2. a) The tiger's stripes help to camouflage it in the long grass and shadows of the forest, but would make it stand out on the plains.

b) A single tiger is easily 'hidden' by its camouflage, but a group would be easier to spot.

c) **Any sensible answer, e.g.:** a group is less likely to be attacked by other animals; it's easier to hunt in a group.

d) **Any sensible answer, e.g.:** it's too hot in the day and much cooler at night; the lions and tigers are more likely to hunt successfully at night as prey can't see them so easily.

Level 6

1. a) Plot A because the radish is fat and looks healthy.

b) i)–ii) Any two from: the weeds may have blocked the light; the weeds may have taken the available water; the weeds may have taken up nutrients from the soil; the weeds may have taken up too much space for the radishes to grow.

c) They wouldn't be able to photosynthesise, so would make less food and grow less than those in the light.

2. a) i) The overall population is rising and the population of poorer countries is increasing much more rapidly than that of the richer countries.

ii) **Any sensible answer, e.g.:** the death rate is higher in poorer countries, so families tend to have more babies; greater birth control in richer countries; poorer countries have more manual labour, so they need more people for work; children are needed to support their families in poorer countries; there is more medicine available in richer countries, so people are living longer.

b) The cost to taxpayers of supporting the ageing population (for pensions and healthcare); less money being earned by the reducing workforce; people may have to work for longer.

Level 7

1. a)

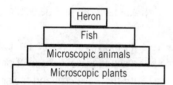

b) The insecticide could have been washed from nearby farmland into streams that feed into the lake. In the lake, the insecticide would have been taken up by the plants from the water. The plants would then be eaten by the animals, so the insecticide would be passed up the chain.

c) Numbers

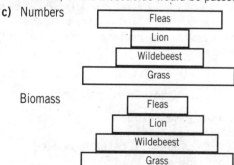

Biomass

Level 8

1. a) Small because the plants were only in the first year of growth.

b) The bigger plants, like grass, were taking the light / water / nutrients / space.

THE ROCK CYCLE

Pages 44–47

Level 3

1. a) C
   b) B
   c) A
   d) D

Level 4

1. a) Fossils
   b) A **should be ticked.**
   c) C **should be ticked.**
   d) B **should be ticked.**

Level 5

1. a) Igneous
   b) The molten rock (magma) would be too hot and would burn up any living things.
   c) Metamorphic
   d) Slate
   e) The river carries the sediment to the sea. It is deposited in layers. The bottom layers are compressed and water is squeezed out. Dissolved salts cement the grains of sediment together.

Level 6

1. a)

Rock	Description of the Rock	Type of Rock
A	Crumbly and contains fossilised sea shells	Sedimentary
B	Hard and contains bands of grey and white interlocking crystals	Metamorphic
C	Very hard and contains large interlocking crystals	Igneous
D	Very hard and contains small interlocking crystals	Igneous

   b) A
   c) C
   d) calcium carbonate + hydrochloric acid ⟶ calcium chloride + water + carbon dioxide

2. a) i) sodium
   ii) chlorine
   b) Two
   c) calcium nitrate; carbon dioxide; water

Level 7

1. a) i) lava
   ii) magma
   b) Igneous
   c) **Any one from:** the crystals at B are larger because they formed more slowly; the crystals at A are smaller because they formed more quickly.
   d) It has lots of holes because the molten rock contained gases.

Level 8

1. a) i)–ii) In any order: there is more rock at A; the rock at A is better insulated by the rock above it.
   b) Sandstone, limestone, granite. The sandstone was made first because it's at the bottom; the limestone formed next and is found on top of the sandstone; the granite then cut through the existing rocks, so it's the youngest.
   c) Marble – metamorphic rock
   d) By high pressure
   e) Pour the acid onto the rock. If it fizzes / bubbles, the rock contains a metal carbonate and it could therefore be limestone.

MAKING SOUND, HEARING SOUND

Pages 48–51

Level 4
1. a) C **should be ticked**.
   b) It vibrates.
   c) It sends impulses to the brain.

Level 5
1. a) Movement in one direction, then in the other.
   b) i) The vibrating strings and wood cause the air to vibrate.
      ii) The vibrations are passed along the air particles. The particles themselves don't travel, they only vibrate. The sound energy travels.
2. a) Hertz (Hz)
   b) The higher the frequency of a note, the higher the pitch of the sound.
   c) High-frequency sounds (i.e. sounds of a frequency too high for human ears to detect).
   d) A pulse of ultrasound is sent towards the sea bed. The longer the time it takes for the echo to come back, the deeper the sea bed.
3. a) They can sense which ear is closer to the sound.
   b) Because the sound travels faster and reaches both ears at almost the same time.
   c) i)–ii) **In any order:** navigation; hunting
   d) Because they use their lower jaw by placing it on the ground to detect vibrations in the ground that they transfer to their internal ears.
   e) Yes, because sound travels faster through the ground.

Level 6
1. a) A vacuum has no particles in it, not even air.
   b) There are no particles to vibrate and transfer the sound energy.
   c) The particles are closer together in water.

2. a) It is the distance from a point on a wave to the exact same point on the next wave (i.e. the length of one wave).
   b) A short wavelength

Level 7
1. a) A particle moves to one side, then to the other side, then back to its original position – it vibrates.
   b) i) Sound energy
      ii) It makes it vibrate.
      iii) The auditory nerve
   c) Loud sounds can damage the ear drum or the nerve endings inside the cochlea in the ear, damaging a person's hearing.

Level 8
1. a) A microphone
   b) A waveform
   c)
   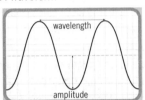
   d) **Any sensible answer, e.g.:**
   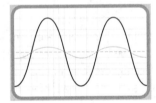
   e) The wave with a smaller amplitude would have a lower volume.
   f) On the waveform, the vibrations are up and down on a single line but a sound wave is made of particles vibrating side to side. Both the waveform and the sound wave have the same wavelength.

ACKNOWLEDGEMENTS

The authors and publisher are grateful to the copyright holders for permission to use quoted materials and images.

Every effort has been made to trace copyright holders and obtain their permission for the use of copyright material. The authors and publishers will gladly receive information enabling them to rectify any error or omission in subsequent editions. All facts are correct at time of going to press.

Letts and Lonsdale
4 Grosvenor Place
London SW1X 7DL

Orders: 015395 64910
Enquiries: 015395 65921
Email: enquiries@lettsandlonsdale.co.uk
Website: www.lettsandlonsdale.com

ISBN: 978-1906415-89-1

01/200309

Published by Letts and Lonsdale

© 2009 Letts and Lonsdale.

British Library Cataloguing in Publication Data.

A CIP record of this book is available from the British Library.

Book Concept and Development: Helen Jacobs
Commissioning Editor: Rebecca Skinner
Authors: Emma Poole, Caroline Reynolds and Bob Woodcock
Project Editor: Richard Toms
Cover Design: Angela English
Inside Concept Design: Helen Jacobs and Sarah Duxbury
Text Design and Layout: Little Red Dog Design
Artwork: Letts and Lonsdale

Printed in Italy

Letts and Lonsdale make every effort to ensure that all paper used in our books is made from wood pulp obtained from well-managed forests, controlled sources and recycled wood or fibre.

2 Rory and Danny are identical twins. Rory has blond hair, blue eyes and is good at football. He enjoys reading, his best subject is maths and he has a scar on his right wrist. Danny has blond hair, blue eyes and is good at rugby. He enjoys playing video games, his best subject is French and he has a scar on his forehead.

a) Which characteristics are caused by Rory and Danny's genes?

b) Which characteristics are caused by their environment?

c) Are there any characteristics that could be influenced by both genes and the environment? Give a reason for your answer.

Level 6

1 The European pond turtle is a reptile that's found in slow-moving water throughout southern Europe and northern Africa. It is now quite rare and is an endangered species.

a) The turtles lay their eggs, which have tough leathery shells, in small holes dug into sand. How does the eggshell help the developing turtle to survive before it hatches?

b) The table below shows the percentage of male and female turtles that hatch when the eggs are incubated at different temperatures.

Temperature (^{0}C)	% Hatching as Males	% Hatching as Females
23	100	0
26	88	12
29	44	56
32	8	92
35	0	100

i) Use the table to suggest how a conservation worker could ensure only females hatch.

ii) At approximately what temperature would roughly equal numbers of both sexes hatch?

iii) Suggest a reason why the conservation worker would need high numbers of females.

2 The ptarmigan is a bird that lives in isolated mountainous areas in Scotland. In the spring and summer its feathers are brown, but it moults them to white ones in the late autumn to winter.

a) Suggest a way in which the white feathers are an advantage to the ptarmigan in winter.

_____

b) Rabbits also live in these areas but have the same colour fur all year round. Fill in the missing words to complete the sentence below.

Rabbits _____ their fur colour from their parents in the form of

_____ that are found in the _____ of the sperm

and egg cells.

Level 7

1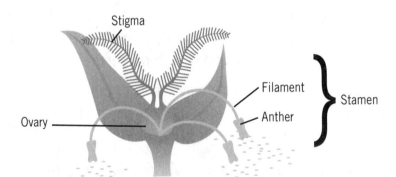

a) Above is a diagram of a typical grass flower. It is pollinated by the wind blowing pollen from the anther of one grass flower to the stigma of another.

i) How is the stamen adapted?

_____

ii) How is the stigma adapted?

_____

b) The stamens and stigma of a flower aren't ripe at the same time. What is the advantage of this?

_____

c) Flowers like buttercups are pollinated by insects, such as bees. Why do these flowers have brightly-coloured petals, unlike grass?

_____

1 The diagram shows a cactus plant. Cacti are adapted to survive in very dry conditions.

a) The leaves of the cactus are reduced to spines. How does this help it to survive?

....

b) The stem is large with a space in the centre. How does this help the cactus to survive?

....

c) The stem is also covered by a thick, waxy layer called the cuticle. How does this help the cactus to survive?

....

d) The root system is long and branching. How does this help the cactus to survive?

....

e) Some plants like marram grass, which grows on sand dunes in Britain, are also adapted to survive in dry places. The leaves of marram grass aren't flat, but are curled up into a shape like that of a drinking straw. How does this help it to survive?

....

....

2 Some mammals are adapted to have a very high rate of respiration to keep warm.

a) Give another reason why these mammals need a high heart rate.

....

b) Why would it be an advantage for these mammals to store a lot of fat?

....

Rocks and Weathering

Level 3

1 Look at the boxes below, which show how four different rocks are used. Draw lines between the boxes to link each rock and its use with the reason why the rock is used.

Rock and its Use

Slate for roof tiles	
Limestone for making statues	
Rock salt for gritting roads 	
Marble for making kitchen worktops 	

Reason why the Rock is Used

- It's easy to carve
- It can be polished to give a smooth, attractive surface
- It's waterproof and can be split into layers
- It lowers the freezing point of water

Level 4

1 Limestone is a sedimentary rock.

a) Which of these statements about sedimentary rocks are true? Tick the two correct options.

   A   They're made when molten rock cools down and solidifies

   B   They will never contain fossils

   C   Marble is an example

   D   Sandstone is an example

   E   They're made of grains that are cemented together

b) Heather wants to find out how the mass of limestone changes when it's placed in water. The diagram shows Heather's experiment.

Mass at Start (g)	1.7
Mass After it has been put into Water (g)	2.1
Difference in Mass (g)	

   i)   Complete the table to show the difference in mass.

   ii) Why does the mass of limestone go up when it's placed in water?

1 A sedimentary rock contains the remains of dead sea animals.

   a) i) What parts of the sea animals are most likely to be preserved in the rock?

     ii) How old are these remains likely to be? Tick the correct option.

      A Days ⬭   **B** Months ⬭   **C** Years ⬭   **D** Thousands of years ⬭

   b) Sedimentary rock can be weathered by water and changes in temperature.

     i) What is the name of this type of weathering?

     ii) Explain what happens in this type of weathering.

2 **a)** What type of rock is sandstone?

   b) Why is rainwater slightly acidic?

   c) Why does rainwater in polluted areas cause rocks to weather faster than they usually do?

   d) Why does limestone weather faster than sandstone?

1 Limestone contains calcium carbonate ($CaCO_3$). Sandstone contains silicon dioxide (SiO_2).

   a) How many atoms are represented in the formula for silicon dioxide?

   b) Caroline placed a piece of limestone and a piece of sandstone into a beaker of water. Why did bubbles appear from each of the rocks?

Limestone   Sandstone

   c) Caroline dried both pieces of rock. She then placed them into a beaker that contained hydrochloric acid. How could she use this experiment to tell the two rocks apart?

2 Coal, oil and natural gas are fossil fuels. Fossil fuels are burned in power stations. The reaction produces carbon dioxide.

a) Name the gas that fossil fuels react with when they're burned.

b) What environmental problem does carbon dioxide contribute to?

c) Many fossil fuels contain traces of sulfur. When sulfur is burned, the gas sulfur dioxide is formed. Write a word equation to sum up the reaction that takes place when sulfur is burned.

d) What environmental problem can be caused by sulfur dioxide?

Level 7

1 Coal is a fossil fuel.

a) Name an element found in fossil fuels.

b) Explain why fossil fuels are described as non-renewable.

c) Why is it difficult to say exactly when the world will run out of fossil fuels?

d) Coal mainly consists of the element carbon. Write a symbol equation to sum up the reaction that takes place when coal is burned in a good supply of oxygen.

2 Rock salt is an evaporate mineral.

a) Describe how the mineral is formed.

b) How would the temperature affect how quickly the mineral was formed?

1 The diagram below shows a cliff face.

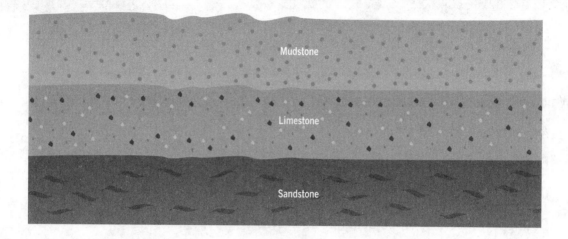

a) Suggest how the mudstone has been formed.

_____

_____

b) Limestone contains the compound calcium carbonate ($CaCO_3$). Sulfuric acid (H_2SO_4) reacts with calcium carbonate. Complete the word and symbol equations to sum up the reaction that takes place.

i) Calcium carbonate + sulfuric acid ⟶ _____ _____ +

_____ + _____

ii) $CaCO_3 + H_2SO_4$ ⟶ _____ + _____ + _____

iii) Nitric acid also reacts with calcium carbonate. One of the products is calcium nitrate, $Ca(NO_3)_2$. How many atoms are represented in the formula for calcium nitrate?

_____

c) The sandstone is examined using a magnifying glass. It contains round grains of quartz that are stuck together.

i) Why are the grains made of quartz?

_____

ii) Suggest how the grains get stuck together.

_____

iii) Suggest how the grains become rounded.

_____

Light Rays

1 Which of the following statements about light are true? Tick the three correct options.

    A Light is a form of radiation   ◯

    B Light is a form of energy   ◯

    C Light rays reflect off your eyes onto objects   ◯

    D Light rays reflect off objects into your eyes   ◯

2 **a)** Which of the following is an example of a luminous object? Tick the correct option.

    A A candle   ◯   **B** A chair   ◯

    C A mirror   ◯   **D** A prism   ◯

    E A shadow   ◯

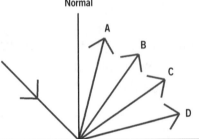

b) Which one of the following paths correctly shows the reflection of a ray of light from a plane mirror?

....

3 The diagram below shows a girl sitting in a glass conservatory.

a) What property of glass allows the girl to be seen?

....

b) What property of the brick wall makes it impossible to see the girl's feet?

....

c) Some windows are made of frosted glass. Frosted glass is described as translucent. What does translucent mean?

....

1 The Moon isn't a luminous object – it doesn't give off its own light.

  a) Explain how it is possible to see the Moon at night.

_____

  b) Stars are also visible in the night sky. Explain how stars are seen.

_____

  c) Give two examples of luminous objects found on Earth.

    i) _____

    ii) _____

2 **a)** Why does a light ray bend when it travels from water to air?

_____

  b) Why does a light ray bend when it travels from air to water?

_____

  c) What is this effect known as?

_____

  d) The diagram below shows the bending of two light rays from a stone on a river bed as the rays leave the water. How does this affect the way that the stone appears to a person standing on the bank of the river?

_____

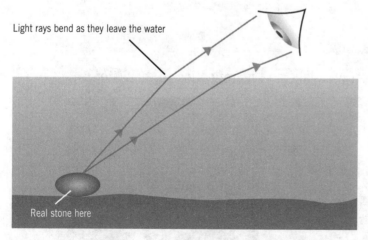

Light rays bend as they leave the water

Real stone here

  e) Add a cross to the diagram to show where the stone appears to be.

1 The diagram shows a cat standing in front of a street light.

a) The cat is opaque. Explain how this fact causes a shadow to be created.

....

b) The shape of the shadow is the same as the shape of the cat. What does this suggest about the way that light travels?

....

c) A person on the street would be able to see the cat. Explain how the street light enables the cat to be seen.

....

d) The moment the street light is switched off, the shadow disappears. What does this tell you about the speed of light?

....

1 The diagram below shows a sunset on a lake and its reflection in the water.

a) Draw a ray of light that shows how a woman standing on the shore sees the sunset directly.

b) Draw rays of light that show how a woman standing on the shore sees the reflection of the sunset in the water.

2 The diagram below shows a sheet of paper highly magnified. Four parallel rays of light hit the paper.

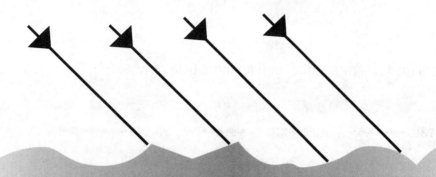

a) i) Complete the diagram to show how the rays of light are reflected off the paper.

ii) What is this effect called?

b) A mirrored surface appears smooth, even when highly magnified. Explain what effect this has on the way that light rays are reflected off its surface.

Level 8

1 a) A spectrum is formed when white light is shone through a prism. What is a spectrum?

b) Explain how this spectrum is formed.

c) A white object reflects all of the light that hits it. What happens to the light that hits a black object?

d) Why does a red object appear red?

Environmental Relationships

1. This is a typical food chain found in and around a field of wheat:

Wheat ⟶ Grasshopper ⟶ Shrew ⟶ Fox

a) Which member of the food chain is an insect?

b) Farmers often spray insecticide onto their crops to kill insects. How would this insecticide get into the insects from the plants?

c) Shrews only live for about 12 months. During that time a female can have 10 litters of about 8 to 10 babies. How does this help to keep up the population of shrews in the field?

d) The shrews' nests are often small burrows in the ground. Why is this better than having the nests on the ground?

2. If you went into a meadow of wild flowers and grasses and wanted to find out about this habitat, you would have to observe various things.

a) Name two non-living conditions you could measure.

i)

ii)

b) It's impossible to count all the different plants, so you would need to sample the field. What could you use to do this?

c) Suggest two pieces of equipment that you might use to catch small insects.

i)   ii)

d) What can you use to look up and identify the different organisms you find?

1 Every year, the Royal Society for the Protection of Birds (RSPB) runs a garden birdwatch count. People are asked to count and record the numbers of different birds that they see in their garden for one hour on a certain date. The results are passed on to the RSPB, which uses the data to compare different years.

a) Why is this kind of birdwatch more reliable than only one person doing it?

b) Give two things that are being controlled in this activity.

i)

ii)

c) If the number of robins was fewer in one year than the year before, could the RSPB claim that the number was falling? Explain your answer.

2 Lions live on the plains, which are mainly grassland with a few trees. Tigers live in forests.

a) How does the appearance of the tiger help it to live in the forest, but would be of no advantage on the plains?

b) Tigers usually hunt their prey alone. Suggest a reason why tigers are solitary animals.

c) Lions tend to stay together in a group called a pride. Suggest a reason why this is an advantage.

d) Both lions and tigers hunt at night. Tigers stay in the shade most of the day. Lions also enjoy the shade and spend most of the day asleep. Suggest a reason for this behaviour.

1 A gardener set up two vegetable plots in the spring and planted seeds. But the person who was supposed to weed the beds only kept one of them free of weeds.

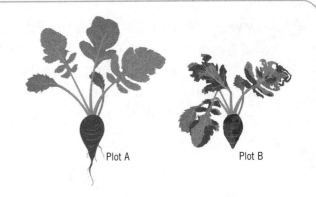

Plot A   Plot B

a) Looking at the radishes opposite, which plot do you think was kept free of weeds? Give a reason for your answer.

....

b) Suggest two ways in which the weeds may have affected the growth of the radishes.

i) ....

ii) ....

c) Plot A got more sun than plot B. How would this affect the radishes in plot B?

....

....

2 The graph opposite shows how the human population of the world has changed over a period of time.

a) i) What conclusion can you make from this information?

....

....

....

....

....

World Population

Population (millions)

6000 –

5000 –

4000 –

3000 –

2000 –

1000 –

0 –

1930   1960   1975   2000

Year

■ Poorer countries
■ Richer industrial countries

ii) Why do you think this is happening?

....

....

....

b) In richer countries, the number of older people is increasing while the birth rate is slowing. What problems might this cause?

....

....

....

Level 7

1 Below is an example of a food chain in a large lake.

Microscopic plants ⟶ Microscopic animals ⟶ Fish ⟶ Heron

a) Sketch the possible pyramid of numbers for this food chain.

b) Scientists discovered a high concentration of an insecticide in all the organisms in this food chain, but none of them are insects. Suggest how it got into the food chain.

_____

_____

c) For the food chain below, draw a pyramid of numbers and a pyramid of biomass.

Grass ⟶ Wildebeest ⟶ Lion ⟶ Fleas on the lion

Level 8

1 The table below shows the numbers of different plants found in an area that was completely bare earth at the start.

Plant	Number After 1 Year	Number After 2 Years	Number After 3 Years
Grass	5	18	20
Violet	15	2	0
Chickweed	30	14	0
Gorse	0	1	1
Hawthorn	0	0	1

a) Suggest the size of the plants in this patch after one year. Give a reason for your answer.

_____

b) Explain why the number of violets and chickweed decreased to 0 over the 3-year period.

_____

The Rock Cycle

1 Look at the diagram opposite that shows part of the rock cycle. Write down the letter for each label below.

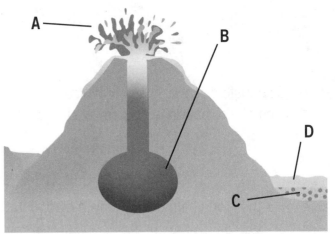

a) Sediment ....

b) Magma ....

c) Lava ....

d) Sea ....

1 There are three types of rock – sedimentary, metamorphic and igneous.
Look at the diagram of the cliff face opposite.

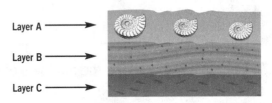

a) Some rocks contain the remains of dead plants and animals. What are these remains called?

....

b) What type of rock is layer A most likely to be? Tick the correct option.

A Sedimentary ⬜   B Metamorphic ⬜   C Igneous ⬜

c) What type of rock is layer A definitely not? Tick the correct option.

A Sedimentary ⬜   B Metamorphic ⬜   C Igneous ⬜

d) Layer B contains rocks that have been changed. What type of rock is layer B? Tick the correct option.

A Sedimentary ⬜   B Metamorphic ⬜   C Igneous ⬜

Level 5

1. The diagram opposite shows a
cross-section through a volcano.

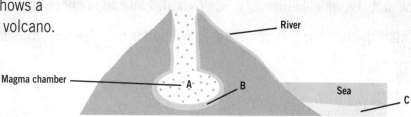

a) The molten rock at A cools down and solidifies. What type of rock is formed at A?

....

b) Explain why the rock formed at A doesn't contain fossils.

....

c) What is the new type of rock formed at B?

....

d) The rock at B used to be called mudstone. What is the name of the new rock?

....

e) Sandstone is formed at C. Describe how sandstone is formed.

....

....

....

Level 6

1. Four different rocks are described below.

a) Complete the table by classifying each rock as **sedimentary**, **metamorphic** or **igneous**.

Rock	Description of the Rock	Type of Rock
A	Crumbly and contains fossilised sea shells	
B	Hard and contains bands of grey and white interlocking crystals	
C	Very hard and contains large interlocking crystals	
D	Very hard and contains small interlocking crystals	

b) Which rock could be limestone? ....

c) Which rock could have formed in a magma chamber? ....

d) Limestone contains calcium carbonate, which reacts with hydrochloric acid. Write a word
equation to sum up the reaction between calcium carbonate and hydrochloric acid.

Level 6 (cont.)

2 Rock salt contains sodium chloride (NaCl). Limestone contains calcium carbonate ($CaCO_3$).

   a) Identify the elements represented in the formula for sodium chloride.

     i) Na is ....

     ii) Cl is ....

   b) How many atoms are represented in the formula for sodium chloride?

     ....

   c) Mickey placed a piece of limestone into a beaker containing nitric acid. Complete the word equation below to sum up the reaction between calcium carbonate and nitric acid.

     calcium carbonate + nitric acid ⟶ .... +

     .... + ...

Level 7

1 The diagram below shows a cross-section through a volcano. The substances at A and at B are both liquid.

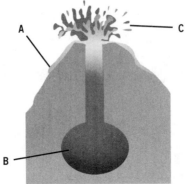

   a) Name the following substances:

     i) A is ....   **ii)** B is ....

   b) What type of rock is formed at A and at B?

     ....

   c) The size of the crystals found in the rocks that form at A are different to the size of the crystals that form at B. Describe the difference and suggest why the crystal sizes are different.

     ....

   d) The molten rock at C cools down and forms a rock called pumice. Pumice has a very low density. Suggest why pumice has a low density.

     ....

1 The diagram below shows a cross-section through a cliff face.

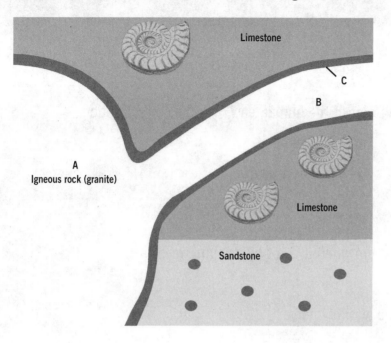

a) The crystals at A formed more slowly than those at B. Suggest two reasons why the crystals formed more slowly at A.

i) ....

ii) ....

b) Place the three rocks – limestone, granite and sandstone – in order of age from the oldest to the youngest. Explain your answer.

....

....

....

c) Suggest the name and type of rock which is found at C.

....

d) Apart from high temperature, suggest how else the limestone could be changed into the rock found at C.

....

e) Scientists who study rocks often carry small bottles of acid. They use the acid to help them identify limestone rocks, which contain calcium carbonate. What would they do with the acid and how would they know the rock could be limestone?

....

Making Sound, Hearing Sound

Level 4

1 a) Which of the following isn't part of the human ear? Tick the correct option.

A The cochlea ◯   **B** The anvil ◯

C The saddle ◯   **D** The stirrup ◯

E The hammer ◯

b) What happens to the ear drum when it is hit by a sound wave?

....

c) What is the function of the auditory nerve?

....

Level 5

1 a) What is meant by the term 'vibration'?

....

b) i) Describe how a violin produces a sound.

....

ii) How does the sound travel through the air?

....

....

2 a) What is the unit of frequency? ....

b) Explain how the frequency of a note affects the pitch of a sound.

....

c) Bats navigate using ultrasound. What is ultrasound?

....

d) Explain how ships can use ultrasound to detect the depth of water beneath them.

....

....

3 a) Your ears can tell the direction that a sound is coming from. How do they do this?

_____

b) Why is it more difficult to detect where a sound is coming from in water?

_____

c) Dolphins and whales use ultrasound to communicate. Name two other ways that they use ultrasound.

i) _____   **ii)** _____

d) Why don't snakes need external ears?

_____

_____

e) Do you think that the method snakes use is a good way of detecting sound? Explain your answer.

_____

Level 6

1 The bell below is in an airtight glass jar. When the air is pumped out of the jar the bell can't be heard.

a) What is a vacuum?

_____

b) Why can't the bell be heard by someone looking at the glass jar?

_____

c) Explain why sound travels faster through water than through air.

_____

2 **a)** What is meant by the wavelength of a wave?

b) Would a sound wave with a high frequency have a long or a short wavelength?

Level 7

1 Look at the diagram below.

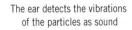
The ear detects the vibrations of the particles as sound

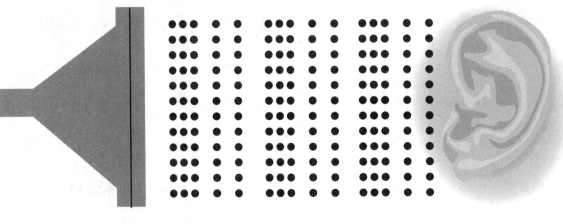

a) Describe the movement of a single air particle as the sound wave travels through the air.

b) **i)** What travels from the loudspeaker to the ear?

ii) What effect does this have on the ear drum in the ear?

iii) What part of the ear sends the information to the brain?

c) Why is it important for people who work with noisy machinery to protect their ears?

1 The diagram below shows the shape of a sound wave as it appears on the screen of an oscilloscope.

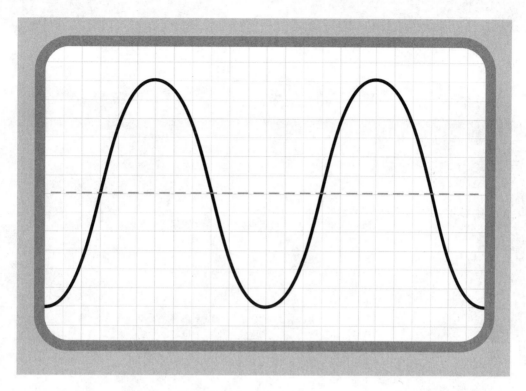

a) What other piece of equipment is needed in order to display a sound wave on the screen of the oscilloscope?

_____

b) What is the name given to the image of the wave on the screen?

_____

c) Show clearly on the diagram the wavelength and the amplitude of the wave.

d) Draw a second wave on the diagram that has a smaller amplitude than the wave shown.

e) How would the sound produced by a wave with a small amplitude compare with the sound produced by a wave with a larger amplitude?

_____

f) The image shown is a model of the actual sound wave produced in the air. State one way in which the image is different from a real sound wave and one way in which it is the same.

_____

_____

_____

Notes

Notes

Periodic Table

Key

Atomic Symbol ⟶ **H**
Name ⟶ hydrogen

Li lithium	**Be** beryllium																**He** helium
Na sodium	**Mg** magnesium											**B** boron	**C** carbon	**N** nitrogen	**O** oxygen	**F** fluorine	**Ne** neon
K potassium	**Ca** calcium	**Sc** scandium	**Ti** titanium	**V** vanadium	**Cr** chromium	**Mn** manganese	**Fe** iron	**Co** cobalt	**Ni** nickel	**Cu** copper	**Zn** zinc	**Al** aluminium	**Si** silicon	**P** phosphorus	**S** sulfur	**Cl** chlorine	**Ar** argon
Rb rubidium	**Sr** strontium	**Y** yttrium	**Zr** zirconium	**Nb** niobium	**Mo** molybdenum	**Tc** technetium	**Ru** ruthenium	**Rh** rhodium	**Pd** palladium	**Ag** silver	**Cd** cadmium	**Ga** gallium	**Ge** germanium	**As** arsenic	**Se** selenium	**Br** bromine	**Kr** krypton
Cs caesium	**Ba** barium	**La** lanthanum	**Hf** hafnium	**Ta** tantalum	**W** tungsten	**Re** rhenium	**Os** osmium	**Ir** iridium	**Pt** platinum	**Au** gold	**Hg** mercury	**In** indium	**Sn** tin	**Sb** antimony	**Te** tellurium	**I** iodine	**Xe** xenon
Fr francium	**Ra** radium	**Ac** actinium	**Rf** rutherfordium	**Db** dubnium	**Sg** seaborgium	**Bh** bohrium	**Hs** hassium	**Mt** meitnerium	**Ds** darmstadtium	**Rg** roentgenium		**Tl** thallium	**Pb** lead	**Bi** bismuth	**Po** polonium	**At** astatine	**Rn** radon